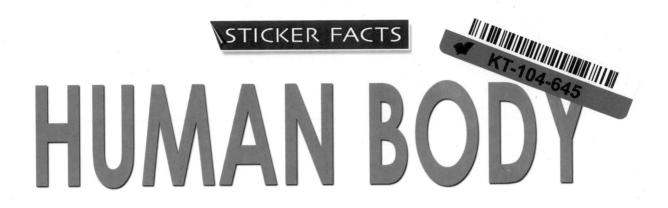

STICKER FACTS

HUMAN BODY

Written by Liz Leask

Published by Top That! Publishing plc
Tide Mill Way, Woodbridge, Suffolk, IP12 1AP, UK
www.topthatpublishing.com
Copyright © 2013 Top That! Publishing plc
0246897531
Printed and bound in China

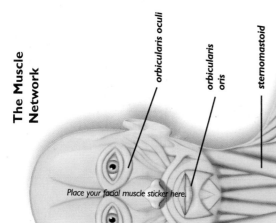

YOUR BODY

Your body is amazing! On the outside, it all looks so simple, but take a look at the inside, and you'll soon realise what an incredibly complicated machine you are! In the pages of this book, you'll find loads of information to help you understand how your body works, and there are also some fabulous stickers you can use to show you how it all fits together.

Growing bodies

Babies' bodies grow and change very fast. Children's bodies are growing all the time. Some people's faces change more than

wrist and finger flexors

The Muscle Network

orbicularis oculi

orbicularis oris

sternomastoid

Place your left chest muscle sticker here.

Place your facial muscle sticker here.

Place your right chest muscle sticker here.

pectoralis major

bicep

rectus abdominus

Every-body!

There are more than seven billion people in the world – that's over 7,000,000,000 different human bodies, of many races, religions, creeds, and colour. There are a quarter of a million babies born each day.

Body systems

Have you been over a busy motorway and looked down, to see many roads all criss-crossing together? Well, your body is a bit like that. It's made

The Muscle Fibre

muscle

bundles of muscle fibre

muscle cell made of myofibrils

myofibril made of actin and myosin filaments

from nine main 'systems' that do separate jobs yet join together at certain points. You'll find out more about these in detail, but they are: skeletal, digestive, muscular, lymphatic, endocrine, nervous, cardiovascular, urinary, and reproductive. Phew!

others as they become grown-ups. When you are about twenty years old, your body will stop growing.

Changing faces

When you look around, you can see that no two people are exactly the same. Although our bodies are basically the same, and we look similar, each of us is unique. The science of genetics explains the similarities and the differences between parents and their children.

sartorius

quadriceps femoris

ankle and foot flexors

HERE'S HOW THE BOOK WORKS!

There are eleven sections in this book and, in each one, you will read some fascinating facts about how a different part of your body works. In each section, you will also find a big picture showing that part of the body —

but parts or all of the picture is missing!

Don't worry! This is where you need to use the fabulous stickers which are in the middle of the book. When you read about a particular part of the body, like the ribcage in the skeleton section, just turn to the sticker pages and look for the ribcage stickers.

Simply put the sticker in the space where the ribcage should be. To complete the picture, all you need to do is read about each part of the body, find the sticker and put it in the right place.

At the end of each section, your head will be full of information, and you will have a great picture to show you what you have just learnt.

In fact, you will be a Sticker Facts Human Body expert!

YOUR SUPER-STRONG SKELETON

The skeleton is your body's frame. Made of strong, hard bones, it gives you shape and protects the soft organs inside you. Unlike the crumbly skeletons which you sometimes see in museums, your bones are very much alive. When a baby is born, it has over 300 bones, but as it becomes a child, its bones grow and join together. By the time it is an adult, the 300 bones will be just 206.

Ball-and-Socket Joint

clavicle

shoulder joint (ball-and-socket joint)

humerus

rounded head fits into cup-shaped cavity

Hinge Joint

humerus

elbow joint (hinge joint)

radius

ulna

The Skeleton

skull

sternum

Place your left rib cage and arm sticker here.

Place your right rib cage and arm sticker here.

clavicle (collarbone)

hip bone

spine

radius

ulna

ribcage

humerus

elbow

Skull

Your skull is the most complicated part of your skeleton and is made up of 22 different bones. The only bone in the skull which moves is the lower jaw bone. The others are all locked together, making a super-strong structure. The skull needs to be extra strong as it protects the most

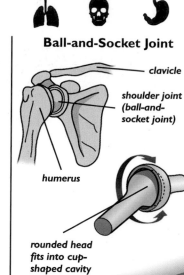

important part of your body, your brain. It also forms the framework of your face, and protects your sense organs – the eyes, ears, nose, and mouth.

Ribs

Some of your most important organs – the heart, lungs and liver are all protected by your ribs. You have 12 pairs of ribs, all attached at your back

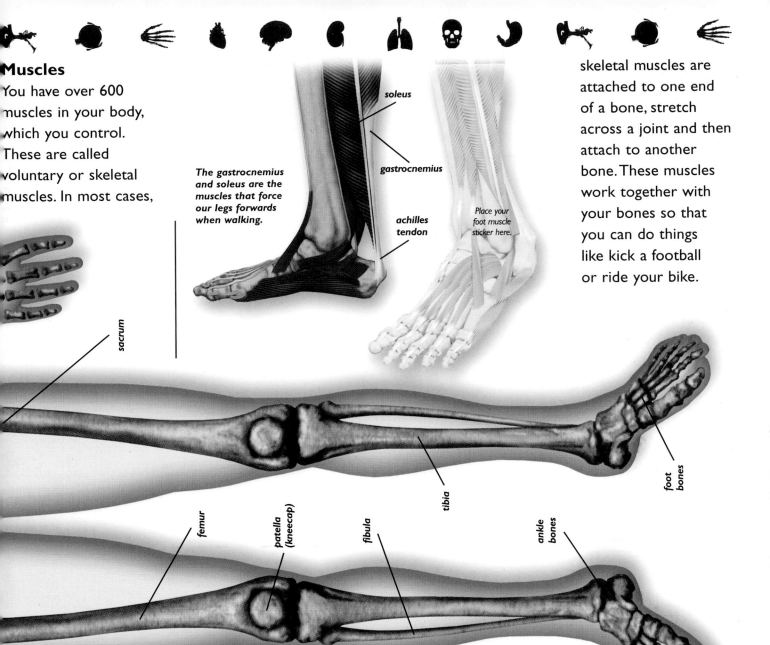

Muscles

You have over 600 muscles in your body, which you control. These are called voluntary or skeletal muscles. In most cases,

The gastrocnemius and soleus are the muscles that force our legs forwards when walking.

soleus

gastrocnemius

achilles tendon

Place your foot muscle sticker here.

skeletal muscles are attached to one end of a bone, stretch across a joint and then attach to another bone. These muscles work together with your bones so that you can do things like kick a football or ride your bike.

sacrum

femur

patella (kneecap)

fibula

tibia

ankle bones

foot bones

to your spine. The top seven pairs of ribs are also attached at the front to your breastbone or sternum, a solid piece of bone in the middle of your chest.

Joints

When two or more bones in your body meet, they make a joint. Different joints move in different ways – some joints, like most of those in the skull, do not move at all. The bone at the top of your arm is round and fits into a cup shape in your shoulder bone, making a ball-and-socket joint. This type of joint lets you move your arm very easily in lots of different directions.

The longest bone

Your leg bones support the weight of your whole body, which is why the longest, strongest bone you have is your thigh bone, or femur.

The smallest bone

The smallest bone in your body is the stirrup or stapes, in your ear.

The most bones

Over half your body's bones are in your hands and feet! Added together, the bones of your feet and ankles, total 52 out of 206!

YOUR HEART AND BLOOD VESSELS

The cells in your body need oxygen and food to live, grow, and work. These essential supplies are delivered by your blood, which constantly travels around in a series of tiny branches or vessels called arteries and veins. But blood cannot travel by itself – it is pumped by one of the busiest organs in your body, your heart. This amazing organ works all day, every day, for the whole of your life.

The Heart

vena cava

aorta

pulmonary artery

left atrium

pulmonary veins

pulmonary valve

Place your atrium and ventricle sticker here.

right atrium

right ventricle

left ventricle

septum

The heart: your most important muscle

You have muscles to kick a ball, blink your eyes and smile, but the most important muscle in your body is your heart. The heart is made of a special type of thick muscle called cardiac muscle or myocardium, which acts like a pump, pushing blood around your body. This pump works all by itself without any instructions from you, and never gets tired.

External heart view.

Valves

Blood is pumped so quickly through your heart, you might think it would be easy for it to lose its way! But there are four small flaps, or valves, in your heart which make sure that the blood always heads in the right direction, and cannot flow back. The mitral and tricuspid valves make sure that blood flows the right way from the atria to the ventricles, while the aortic and pulmonary valves control the blood as it leaves the heart.

HEART FACTS

Your heart is about the size of a clenched fist and sits just to the left of the middle of your chest. It works so hard, that every 20 seconds the left ventricle manages to pump fresh blood to every one of the billions of cells in your body. It beats about 70 times a minute, and every day it pumps about 7,000 litres of blood!

The septum

The two halves of your heart are separated by a thick wall of muscle called the septum. Each half has a different job to do. The right half of your heart receives blood from your body, then pumps it into the lungs so that it can receive fresh oxygen. The left side does the opposite: blood packed with oxygen comes in from the lungs and is then pumped out into the body.

The chambers

Your heart is divided into two halves and each half has two different areas, or chambers. The top two chambers are called the atria and the bottom two are called the ventricles. The great thing

Red blood cells.

about your atria and ventricles is that they work as a team. When blood comes back to the heart from the body or lungs, it fills up the atria, then passes from the atria to the ventricles. The ventricles pump blood out of the heart, while the atria refill, ready for the next beat.

Blood vessels

When blood leaves your heart, it goes on an amazing journey through a huge network of arteries and veins. Your arteries carry blood full of oxygen away from the heart, the veins carry blood back. If all the blood vessels in your body were put together, they would measure about 100,000 km long.

Place your red blood cells sticker here.

Place your white blood cells sticker here.

White blood cells.

Blood Circulation

Place your blood circulation upper body sticker here.

pulmonary arteries

pulmonary veins

main veins back to heart

main veins from heart

White blood cells

White cells help your body fight infection. There are many different types.

Red blood cells

Red cells carry oxygen and live for about 120 days. New ones are produced in your bone marrow.

Long journey

Your blood travels a very long way on its journey around your body. The blood vessels in your body, if stretched out end-to-end, would reach around the world twice!

BREATHING

Oxygen is in the air that's all around us. The system which makes sure our bodies receive a fresh, constant supply is called the respiratory system, which moves air in and out of our bodies by breathing. Air enters through the nose and mouth, then travels down into the lungs, where oxygen is taken out and goes into your blood. The leftover air is pushed out of the lungs – and then the process starts all over again.

Lungs

The main organs in your respiratory system are your two lungs, which take up most of the space inside your chest. Unlike other pairs of organs in your body, such as your eyes, your lungs are not the same size and shape. The left lung is slightly smaller, and is shaped to make room for your heart. On the outside, the lungs look like soft, pink sponges, but on the inside they are full of the tubes and air sacs which feed oxygen into your body.

The larynx and epiglottis

On the way to the lungs, air goes through the voice box or larynx, which also plays an important part in breathing. Inside the larynx there is a flap called the epiglottis. When you are eating, the epiglottis covers the larynx to make sure that no food can escape down into the lungs. But when you are not eating, the epiglottis opens up, leaving the larynx as a clear airway.

Mighty muscles

The muscle which provides power for your respiratory system is called the diaphragm. It sits underneath your lungs and works with the muscles between your ribs to help you breathe. When you breathe in, your diaphragm moves downwards,

The Breathing Mechanism of the Human Body

nasal passages

trachea

lung

bronchiole

diaphragm

oesophagus

bronchi

alveoli

Place your lung sticker here.

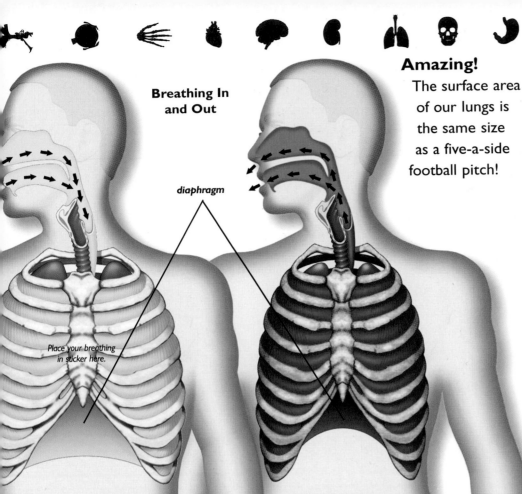

Breathing In and Out

diaphragm

Place your breathing in sticker here.

Amazing!
The surface area of our lungs is the same size as a five-a-side football pitch!

Alveoli

There are millions of alveoli in your lungs. Each one is covered with microscopic blood vessels called capillaries. The oxygen in the air passes through these capillaries into red blood cells and this new blood, full of fresh oxygen, is pumped around the body by the heart. Unwanted air passes from the blood into the alveoli and leaves the body when you breathe out.

and your rib muscles move out. Your chest gets bigger, giving your lungs enough room to fill up with air. When you breathe out, your muscles go back to their normal place, your chest gets smaller and the air from your lungs is pushed out.

The nose knows

The first stop on the breathing route is the nose. Air is sucked in through your nostrils, into a space called the nasal cavity and then it

dives down toward the lungs. But there is something else that happens in the nose. It gets the air ready for the lungs by warming it up, adding moisture and filtering out any nasty dirt.

Windpipe, bronchi and bronchioles

The windpipe, or trachea, is a long tube going straight down to the lungs. When it gets there, it splits into two large tubes called bronchi – one heading off into each lung. Inside the lungs, the bronchi split and divide into

smaller bronchi, a little bit like the branches on a tree. These divide into even smaller tubes – bronchioles – ending in clumps of minute air sacs called alveoli.

Alveoli

bronchiole

alveolus

THE BRILLIANT BRAIN AND NERVOUS SYSTEM

Your brain is the control centre of your body. It teams up with your spinal cord, which runs through the middle of your spine and your nerves to make up your body's nervous system: the communication network which controls everything you do. The brain is divided into different areas, and each area controls particular actions, as well as things like your memory and personality.

Hypothalamus

In the centre of your brain is a tiny area called the hypothalamus, which makes up only 0.3% of your brain's weight. Although very small, the hypothalamus has the important job of making sure that your body stays at the right temperature. When you are cold, the hypothalamus tells your body to shiver so that you start to warm up; when you are too hot, tells your body to swea so that you cool down.

The Nervous System

brain

cranial nerves

cervical nerves

lumbar nerves

Place your nervous system in head sticker here.

spinal cord

spinal nerves

Cerebrum

The biggest part of your brain is the cerebrum, and this is where all your thinking takes place. It makes up about 85% of your brain's weight, and is divided into two halves, with one half on either side of your head. The right half of the cerebrum controls the left side of your body, and the left half the right side! The cerebrum controls lots of actions like writing and speech, and even how good you are at maths!

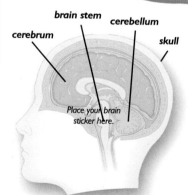

cerebrum

brain stem

cerebellum

skull

Place your brain sticker here.

Cerebellum

The second biggest area of your brain is called the cerebellum, which sits snugly at the back of your brain, tucked underneath the cerebrum. Just like the other parts of the brain, it has a number of important and specific jobs to do. It controls your balance, coordinates the way your muscles move and also makes sure that you are able to sit and stand up straight!

pinal cord

our spinal cord is a
ttle bit like a motorway.
very day, there are
iillions of messages
ravelling up and down
, going to and from the
rain and the rest of
your
body. It is
connected
to your
brain by the
rain stem, and to the

rest of the body by 31
pairs of spinal nerves.
Neatly protected in the
middle of the spine, an
adult's spinal cord will
measure about 43 cm
long and 2.5 cm wide.

Nervous System

Nerve fibres form
a huge network
throughout your body,
and if they were all
joined together, they
would measure about

75 km long!
The longest
nerve in your
body is the
sciatic nerve,
which runs
from your spinal
cord down your
leg. Nerve signals
travel at amazing
speeds through
your nervous
system, sometimes as
fast as 400 km/h.

Nerve Cells

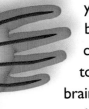

axon

dendrites

cell body

sacral nerves

Spinal Cord

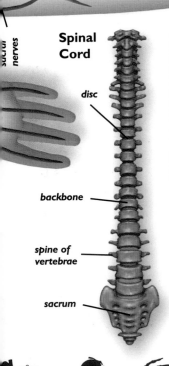

disc

backbone

spine of vertebrae

sacrum

Brain stem

Under the cerebrum
and cerebellum is the
brain stem, which is
connected to the spinal
cord. The brain stem
ensures that the basic
things your body needs
to stay alive work. The
brain stem also links
the spinal cord and the
rest of the brain, making
sure that all essential
messages get through.

How the Brain Works

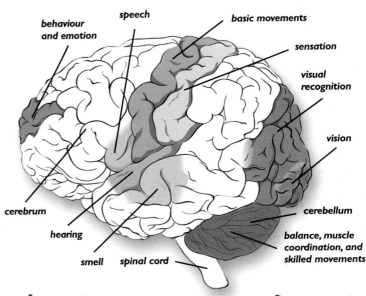

behaviour and emotion
speech
basic movements
sensation
visual recognition
vision
cerebrum
hearing
cerebellum
smell
spinal cord
balance, muscle coordination, and skilled movements

DIGESTIVE SYSTEM

Hmm, think of your favourite foods. Pizza? Pasta? Chocolate? Delicious when you take that first bite, but what happens next? Inside your body, your food goes on an amazing journey from your mouth, and on into your stomach then the intestines. All with the help of some major organs on the way.

The mouth

Your nose smells food, your eyes see it and your body gets ready to eat by producing saliva in your mouth. As you chew, your food is broken down into small lumps and gets mixed with saliva, which breaks down chemicals in the food. Your tongue rolls the, by now squishy food, into a special lump called a bolus, and pushes it to the back of the throat, where it is swallowed down.

Oesophagus

When the bolus has been swallowed, it goes past the windpipe, where air goes into, and out of, your lungs. A special flap called the epiglottis covers the windpipe, so that your food doesn't go down the wrong way. Instead, the bolus heads on down the foodpipe or oesophagus. Here, the muscles squeeze the bolus along, until it reaches your stomach.

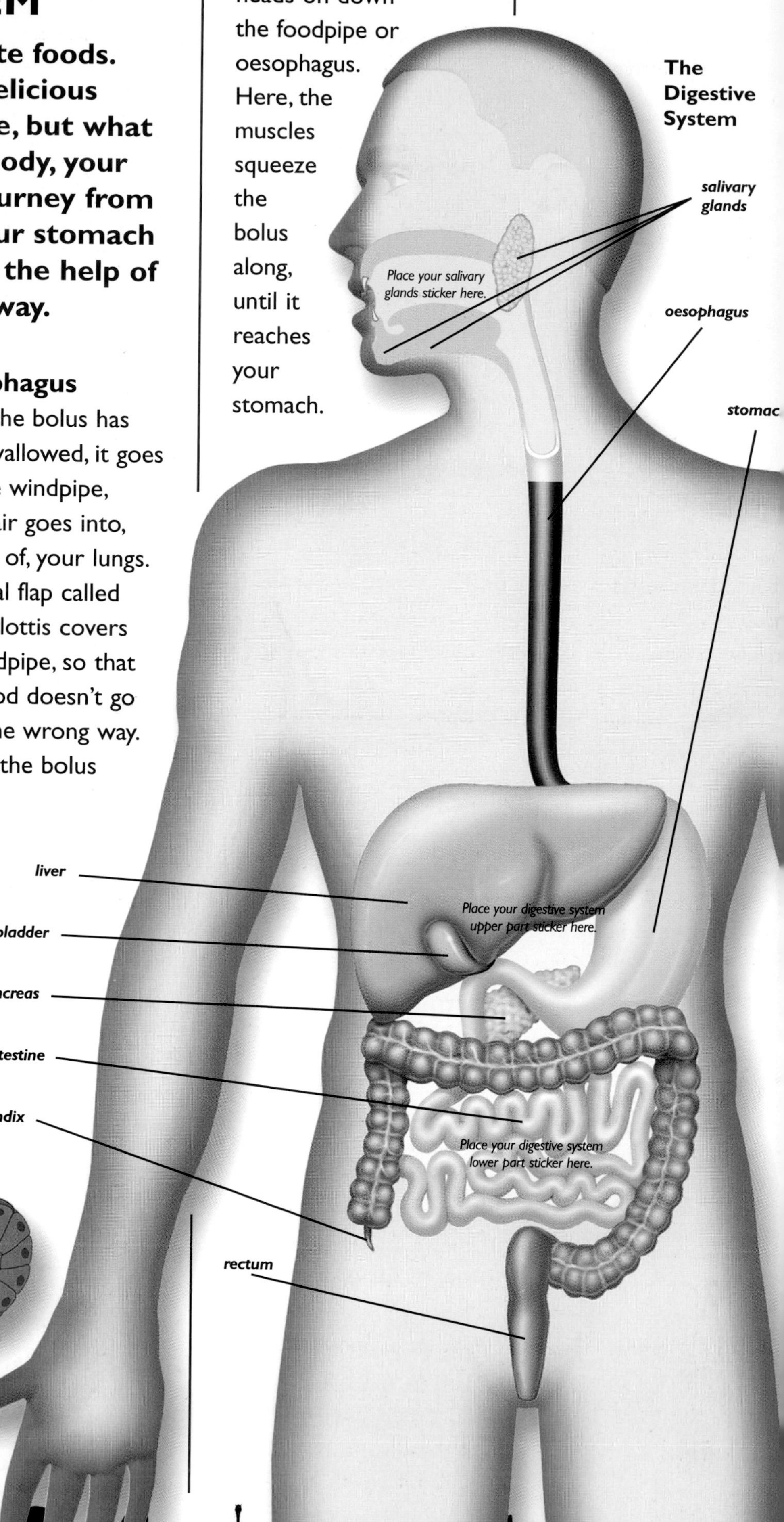

The Digestive System

salivary glands

Place your salivary glands sticker here.

oesophagus

stomac

liver

gall bladder

pancreas

small intestine

appendix

Place your digestive system upper part sticker here.

Place your digestive system lower part sticker here.

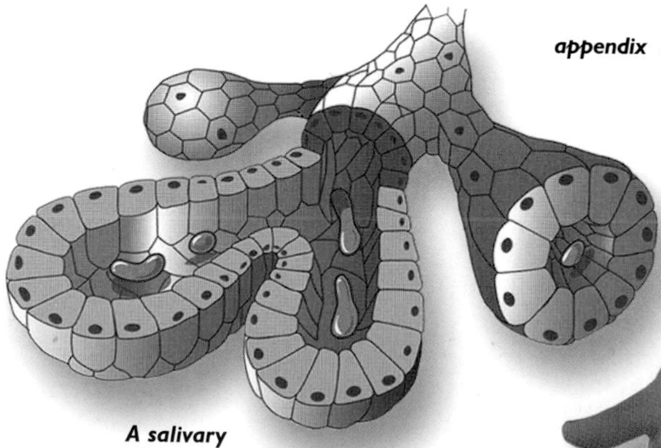

rectum

A salivary gland.

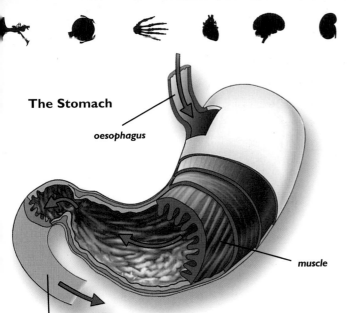

The Stomach

oesophagus

muscle

small intestine

The stomach

Food stays in your stomach for a few hours and, while it is there, the muscles in the stomach wall constantly move, breaking down the food into smaller and smaller pieces. At the same time, strong, acidic liquids called gastric juices get to work on the food, until it is nothing more than a gloopy, thick, soup-like liquid, called chyme. When you are sick, it is chyme which is forced back out of your body by your stomach.

Small intestine

The small intestine is the next step in the digestion process. Here, digestive liquids sent from the liver, pancreas and gall bladder break the

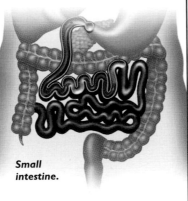

Small intestine.

food down into the important parts, or nutrients, your body needs for energy and to stay healthy, such as vitamins and minerals. These nutrients pass through the wall of the small intestine and into your blood.

The Liver

hepatic vein

gall bladder

Large intestine

When the small intestine has finished taking the nutrients from your food, all that is left is a liquid waste, which passes into the large intestine. As it travels through the large intestine, water and any remaining minerals are taken out of the liquid, so it becomes harder and drier, until it eventually becomes solid waste, or faeces. This solid moves on into the rectum, and finally leaves your body through your anus.

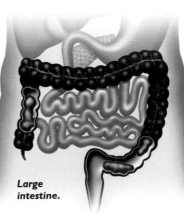

Large intestine.

The liver

From the small intestine, the blood, full of its new nutrients, takes a sharp turn straight to the liver. The liver has two important jobs: firstly, it creates a liquid called bile, which it sends to the small intestine and this helps the body to absorb fats into the bloodstream. Secondly, the liver processes all nutrients delivered to it, taking out anything which may be harmful.

The Pancreas

bile duct

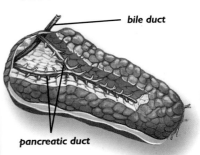

pancreatic duct

Pancreatic juices

The digestive system relies on the pancreas to help with the breakdown of the food we eat. Enzymes break down the food while bile comes from the liver, via the gall bladder. Pancreatic juices come from the pancreas and then intestinal juice is made in the small intestine to further aid digestion.

URINARY SYSTEM

There are two types of waste that are produced by your body. One is solid waste or faeces, which happens when your body has finished digesting food; the other is liquid waste, or urine. The system which deals with this in your body is called the urinary system. There are four main stages in the urinary system: ureters, bladder, urethra, and, most important of all, the kidneys.

Blood is carried by a special blood vessel, called the renal artery, from your heart to your kidneys. The kidneys then get to work on the blood, sieving, filtering, and cleaning it, and the waste products leave your body as urine.

Ureters

The concentrated liquid produced by your kidneys is urine. Your kidneys are able to clean and filter an astonishing 180 litres of blood every day, but from this, only about 2 litres of urine are produced. Coming out of each

About the kidneys

Some of the organs in your body are more important than others and the kidneys are right near the top of the list! They are bean-shaped organs, each about 11–14 cm long, and are at the back of your body at the base of your ribcage. Although most people have two kidneys, it is possible to live with just one. If one of your kidneys stops working, the other one will get bigger so that it can take over and do the work of two.

What do the kidneys do?

Their most important job is to remove any unwanted fluids and waste from your body by cleaning your blood.

The Kidney

renal artery

renal capsule

renal vein

ureter

kidney, is a long tube called the ureter. Every day and every night, there is a constant slow flow of urine from the kidneys, through the ureters and into the bladder.

The Waste Management System

vein

Place your kidney sticker here.

kidneys

ureter

Place your bladder sticker here.

bladder

urethra

Bladder

Your bladder is a stretchy, muscular bag which can expand to store 300–350 ml of urine. When it is full, it sends a message to your brain to tell you that you need to go to the toilet; the muscles squeeze, and the bladder empties. Up to the age of about two, the body automatically gets rid of urine, which is why babies wear nappies!

Rectum

The rectum consists of a muscular tube lined with a special membrane known as epithelium. Faeces are stored in the rectum and contain undigested food such as fibre, dead cells, bacteria, bile and water. The sphincter muscle at the base of the rectum contracts to tell us it needs emptying.

WATER WORKS

You need to drink approximately 1.2 litres of water every day for your kidneys, bladder, and bowel to work efficiently.

The Urinary System

artery

vein

collecting duct

Super mini filters

Each of your kidneys has over one million super mini-filter tubes called nephrons, which are so small they can only be seen with a high-powered microscope. Blood entering the kidney flows straight into the nephrons, where it is filtered. Nutrients and most of the water are taken back by the blood, while the remaining excess water and waste make a concentrated liquid. This trickles down special tubules to the ureter.

Urethra

Urine leaves the body through a tube called the urethra. Urine is 95% water and you may notice that sometimes it is very light, and at other times it is darker. If you have been exercising, haven't drunk very much water, or have been very sweaty, your urine will be darker. If you have been drinking a lot, the extra fluid will pass through your body as urine, and it will be lighter.

The Male Urethra

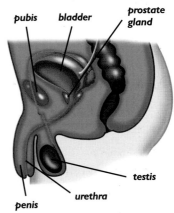

pubis   bladder   prostate gland

testis

urethra

penis

The Female Urethra

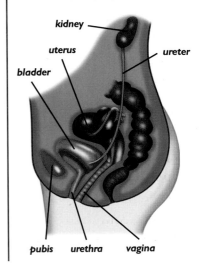

kidney

uterus   ureter

bladder

pubis   urethra   vagina

THE SKIN

Your skin is an amazing thing. It is your body's biggest organ, weighing up to 4 kg and, if it was spread out, it would cover an area up to 22 square feet! Skin covers our whole body, protecting our bones, muscles and organs from germs and damage. It is sensitive to touch, helps to keep our body at the right temperature, and is also waterproof.

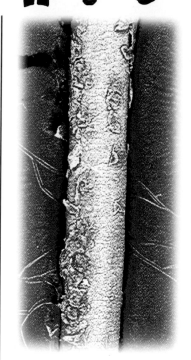

A close-up of a hair.

The epidermis

The very top layer of the skin is the epidermis, which is made of dead, flattened skin cells. We all lose thousands of skin cells from our epidermis every day – in fact, most of the dust lying around your house is made from dead skin cells. But you needn't worry! Underneath the epidermis is a layer of new cells, which move up to the surface, where they harden and die, producing a tough new layer of skin.

The dermis and beyond

Beneath the epidermis, is the living dermis. It contains glands, hair follicles, nerve endings and lots of tiny blood vessels, which bring yo skin the nutrients and oxygen it needs to live and grow. Finally, there is the subcutaneous layer. This is made up mostly of special fatty cells which help to keep your body warm. When you bump against something, the subcutaneous layer also absorbs some of the impact, protecting your body underneath.

Cross-section of the Skin

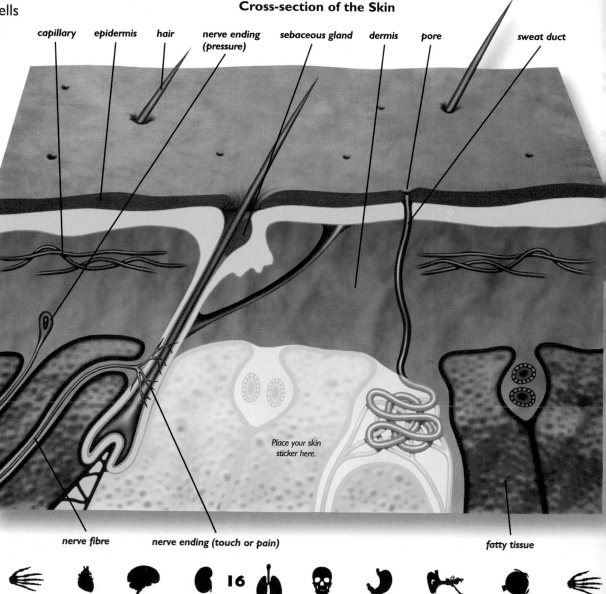

capillary   epidermis   hair   nerve ending (pressure)   sebaceous gland   dermis   pore   sweat duct

Place your skin sticker here.

nerve fibre   nerve ending (touch or pain)   fatty tissue

Nerves

Your skin contains a number of different types of nerve endings, which sense what is happening on the outside. They detect cold, warmth, a light touch from a friend, or something which is painful, then send messages back to your brain to tell it what they're feeling. If it is something painful, like when you pick up a hot cup, the brain instantly responds by telling your muscles to move your hand away, stopping the pain.

Picking up a hot drink will trigger a reflex reaction.

Sebaceous gland

So what do you think it is that makes your skin waterproof? Well, your body has lots of organs called glands which release chemicals to do particular jobs. Buried in your dermis are sebaceous glands, whose job is to produce your skin's own oil, called sebum. Sebum coats both your skin and your hair, keeping them waterproof and protecting them, too.

Hair

Every single hair on your body grows out of a special tube called a follicle, which starts way down in the subcutaneous layer. Each follicle is surrounded by touch-sensitive nerve endings, and they also have their own minute sebaceous gland, which provides sebum to waterproof hair and gives it shine. There are hair follicles on just about every part of your body, and some areas have more than others: your scalp has at least 100,000!

A Touch Receptor

hair

Place your touch receptor sticker here.

sensors around hair detect light touch

Touch

There are seven different types of nerve endings, and they are known as touch receptors. Your fingertips, lips and tongue are some of the most sensitive parts of your body.

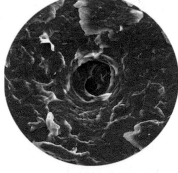

Close-up of the skin showing a pore – a small opening through which water passes as sweat to cool the body down.

Temperature control

When you are too hot, blood vessels in the dermis get rid of some of your body's heat by taking warm blood to the surface of your skin. Your dermis also contains sweat glands, and when you are hot, these produce sweat to cool you down. If you are cold, your blood vessels take the warm blood away from the surface, and tiny muscles at the bottom of your hair follicles make the hairs stand on end, to keep in warmth.

HAIR RAISING

Hair grows at a rate of around 1 mm every three days. Beards are the fastest-growing hairs on the human body. If the average male did not shave, his beard would grow to 10 m long in a lifetime.

HEARING AND BALANCE

You may think that your ears are just the two big, flappy bits you see on the side of your head. Think again! Your ear is made of three different areas: the outer, middle and inner ear, which all work together so that you can hear the sounds around you. But your ears are not just responsible for hearing – they also make sure that you are able to keep your balance.

Attached to this is the anvil bone, and the final ossicle, the stirrup, is joined to the anvil. Sound waves travel down the ear canal and hit the eardrum, making it vibrate.

The vibrations carry on through the ossicles and into the inner ear.

malleus

incus

oval windo

eardrum

stape

Outer ear

Sound travels as invisible waves through the air. Your ears work in pairs to collect the waves and turn them into nerve signals which your brain can understand. Sound waves are first picked up by your outer ear, which is made up of the ear flap and the ear canal. The ear flap directs the sound waves into the ear canal, and from here they travel on to the middle ear.

Middle ear: eardrum and ossicles

Inside the middle ear are the eardrum, a thinly stretched piece of skin, and three tiny bones, the ossicles. The eardrum is attached to the first ossicle, the hammer.

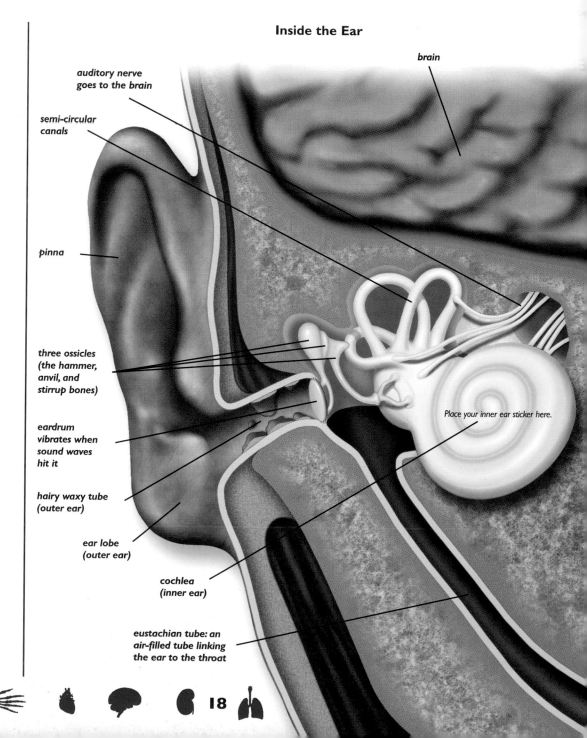

Inside the Ear

brain

auditory nerve goes to the brain

semi-circular canals

pinna

three ossicles (the hammer, anvil, and stirrup bones)

eardrum vibrates when sound waves hit it

hairy waxy tube (outer ear)

ear lobe (outer ear)

cochlea (inner ear)

Place your inner ear sticker here.

eustachian tube: an air-filled tube linking the ear to the throat

Sound Waves Travelling into the Ear

stapes

incus

malleus

ound waves

cochlear nerve

cochlea

ardrum

round window

hair-like receptor cells

Ear wax

Inside the skin lining the ear canal, are ceruminous glands, which produce some of our body's yuckiest stuff – ear wax. Actually, ear wax does a very important job. It forms

Place your earwax sticker here.

Earwax forms a protective layer in the ear.

a protective layer in the ear, trapping dirt and dust and keeping this away from the eardrum. The wax moves to the outside, taking all these horrible bits with it, and leaving your ear canal clean.

Middle ear and eustachian tube

Connected to the middle ear is the eustachian tube. These two organs work together to keep the air pressure the same on both sides of your eardrum, making sure that it works properly and doesn't get damaged. The

A yawn is a deep involuntary breath.

eustachian tube is usually closed, except when you swallow or yawn. If you have ever felt your ears go pop, then you have felt your eustachian tubes opening to balance the air pressure.

Cochlea

The next stop on the sound journey is in the inner ear at the cochlea, a tiny tube filled with liquid and lined with thousands of tiny hairs. The sound vibrations from the ossicles make the liquid in the cochlea vibrate. As it does this, the hairs move, and the sound vibrations are changed into nerve signals so that the brain can understand the sound the ear is hearing.

Athletes can fine-tune their ability to balance to enable them to perform outstanding, skilful feats.

Keep your balance

Just above your cochlea, are three loops, the semicircular canals, and these are organs which keep your balance. They are filled with liquid and lined with very sensitive minute hairs. When your body moves, the liquid flows around the canals. The hairs sense this movement and send signals to the brain telling it about the position of your body. The brain sends instructions to your muscles to make sure that you keep your balance.

Speed of sound

Sound waves travel at an amazing 343 metres per second!

THE MOUTH

Together, your mouth, lips, teeth and tongue make an unbeatable team. Just think what they do. Your mouth is the first stop on the road to digestion, working with your teeth and tongue to chew food. It is also an entry point into your body for all-important air. By working together with your throat, these four organs enable you to shout, scream, laugh and talk.

The mouth

Your mouth contains lots of different organs, including gums, teeth, and tongue. The top, or roof, of your mouth is hard, but the side and bottom are made of soft tissue, including muscle. This gives your mouth lots of flexibility and means it can do all the things it needs to, like eating and talking. Your mouth is also home to three sets of salivary glands, where saliva is made.

Time for a bite

Take a look inside your mouth, and you will see that your teeth are different sizes and shapes. This is because they do different jobs. At the front of your mouth are eight small, flat incisors: four on the top, four on the bottom. On either side of your incisors, are four pointy canines: two on the top, two on the bottom. You use these to rip, chop and cut your food when you first bite it.

Behind the canines are eight premolars, four on the top, four on the bottom. These are bigger than canines and have ridges to crush and grind food. At the back of your mouth are eight giant molars. Stronger even than premolars, the molars give food a final mash before it is swallowed. When you get older, a further four molars, called wisdom teeth, may also grow.

The Mouth

- uvula
- hard palate
- tongue
- wisdom tooth
- second molar
- first molar
- second premolar
- first premolar
- canine
- lateral incisor
- central incisor
- soft palate
- tonsil

Place your right teeth sticker here.

UNIQUE TONGUE

Everyone of us has a unique tongue print, in the same way that everyone has a unique fingerprint.

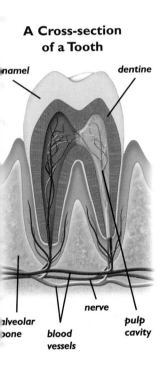

What is a tooth made of?

Your teeth are made of three layers. Coating the outside, is enamel, the hardest material in your body. Underneath the enamel is a strong dentine layer. Its job is to protect the central part of the tooth, the pulp, which

A Cross-section of a Tooth

enamel dentine

alveolar bone blood vessels nerve pulp cavity

contains vessels bringing blood to the tooth so it can stay healthy and grow. Teeth are divided into two parts: above the gum is called the crown and the part underneath is the root. In adults, the roots of the teeth are usually longer than the crowns.

The Tongue

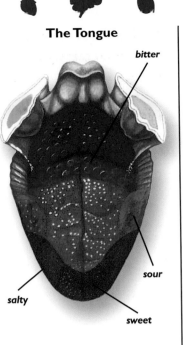

bitter
salty
sour
sweet

Tongue

Your tongue is multi-talented. It is covered in 2,000–8,000 taste buds so that you can enjoy the different foods you eat. It works with your teeth to mix your food with saliva and then swallow it. Without your tongue, you'd find it very hard to talk. The tongue even has an in-built safety mechanism to stop you from swallowing it: this is the frenulum, a thin piece of tissue attaching the underneath of your tongue to the bottom of your mouth. The tongue is a very flexible part of the body.

Structure of the Mouth

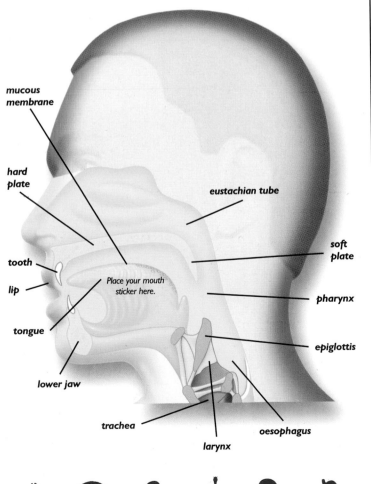

mucous membrane
hard plate
tooth
lip
tongue
lower jaw
trachea
larynx
oesophagus
epiglottis
pharynx
soft plate
eustachian tube

Place your mouth sticker here.

The Larynx

thyroid cartilage
trachea (windpipe)

Voice

At the top of your windpipe, which carries air to and from your lungs, is your voice box or larynx, which contains two rubbery vocal chords. Air forced from the lungs up the windpipe goes through the vocal chords, making them vibrate. This vibration produces a sound, and your throat, mouth, teeth, tongue, and lips work together to form words.

Smile!

It takes 30 muscles to smile and 40 to frown – so be happy to look years younger!

TASTE AND SMELL

Your sense of taste and sense of smell work closely together. Your tongue has thousands of tiny taste buds to detect the different foods you eat, but needs the nose's sense of smell to properly identify all the flavours it comes across. This is why you often can't taste food when you have a cold – your sense of smell isn't working properly, and your poor tongue just can't do all the work by itself.

The taste of fruit is sweet or sour depending on how ripe it is.

this starts to break dow the chemicals in food. T microvilli are stimulate by the saliva, they dete tastes and send nerve messages to your brain which then identifies what the tastes are.

Enjoy what you eat

Appreciating tastes help your body to keep a go chemical balance. Eating sugary and salty foods

Papillae

The top of your tongue looks, and feels, rough because it is covered with bumps called papillae. You have four main types of papillae: fungiform and filiform papillae are at the front of your tongue, foliate and vallate papillae at the back. These strange bumps are very important: they help you eat your food by gripping it and all around them are your taste buds.

How do those taste buds work?

Each of your taste buds has between 50 and 100 special cells. Sticking out of each of these cells are tiny taste hairs called microvilli. When you chew your food, it mixes with saliva, and

How Does the Tongue Taste?

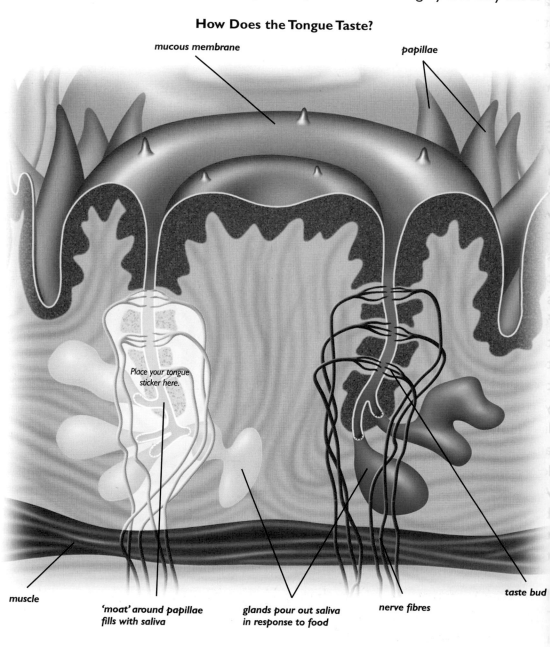

mucous membrane

papillae

Place your tongue sticker here.

muscle

'moat' around papillae fills with saliva

glands pour out saliva in response to food

nerve fibres

taste bud

eets your body's need or carbohydrates and minerals, while eating emons or oranges provides essential itamins. Taste buds also protect your body. If ou eat something which s poisonous or rotten, t will probably taste orrible and you will spit it out. By doing this, aste buds are topping bad ood getting to our stomach and making you ill.

Smell's good!

Without your sense of smell, food just would not taste the same. This is because the smell released by food combines with the tastes detected by your tongue to give you a complete flavour. When you have a bad cold, the lining of your nose swells and you temporarily lose your sense of smell. Although your taste buds continue to work, the food you eat will taste of very little.

Five main flavours

Taste buds can detect five main flavours: sweet, sour,

salty, bitter, and a recently discovered flavour, umami, which is found in the salts of particular acids. Different areas of the tongue can detect

different tastes. Bitter tastes like coffee are detected at the back of the tongue, while sour tastes like lemon are detected on the sides of the tongue. The tip of the tongue recognises sweet tastes, and salt is tasted along both sides at the front.

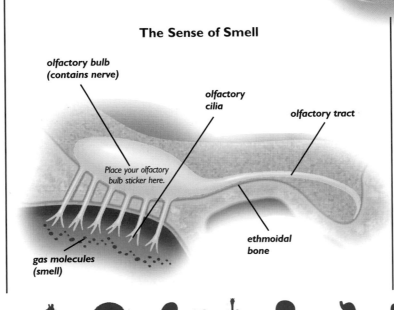

Salty (crisps), sour (lemons) and sweet (honey) flavours can be detected by taste buds.

The Sense of Smell

olfactory bulb (contains nerve)

olfactory cilia

olfactory tract

Place your olfactory bulb sticker here.

ethmoidal bone

gas molecules (smell)

It's a matter of taste

As you grow older your sense of smell becomes duller. In fact, by the time you reach the age of 60, you will have lost around half of your taste buds.

How does the nose smell?

Tucked inside your nose, on an organ called the olfactory bulb, are loads of cilia - miniscule hairs which are covered with cells sensitive to smells in the air. When a smell enters your nose, it hits the cilia which produce nerve signals. These travel along the sensitive cells to a nerve in front of your brain. The brain deciphers the nerve signals and decides what the smell is.

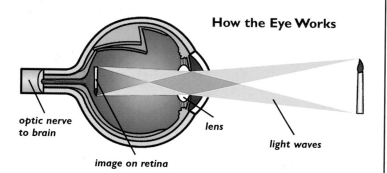

SIGHT

A Cutaway View of the Eye

Each of your eyes is like a well-designed camera allowing you to view the outside world from just a very small chamber. Your eyes are situated deep in eye sockets to protect them.

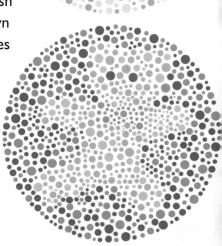

muscle

retina

cornea (clear outer layer)

iris

pupil

Place your eye sticker here.

lens

optic nerve

Pupil

Light bounces off everything you see. When you look at an object, light from it enters your eye through the pupil (this is the black dot in the middle of your eye). When it is dark, your pupils grow bigger to let in as much light as possible; when it is bright, they grow smaller to protect your eye. The pupil's size is changed by muscles in the iris, the coloured part of your eye.

Lens

Now we get to the parts of the eye we can't see! After light enters the pupil, it travels inside the eye and hits a colourless disc – the lens. The lens bends the light, sending an upside-down picture of what you are looking at to the back of the eyeball, the retina.

How the Eye Works

optic nerve to brain

lens

image on retina

light waves

Retina

Inside the retina, are millions of tiny light-sensitive cells called rods and cones. Rods can only see in black and white, while cones see in colour, but working together they process the picture, changing it into nerve signals which are sent back to the brain. The brain pieces together the information to understand what the eyes are seeing.

Colour blindness

About 10% of men and 0.5% of women are colour blind. The most common form of this makes it hard to distinguish between red, brown and green. Your eyes can be tested for colour blindness by covering one eye and looking at a special Ishihara test plate composed of a series of coloured dots, some in object shapes.

Can you see the train and the teddy bear?

Illustrations by: Stephen Sweet, Visual Language library, SGA and Beehive. Photography by: page 7 (bottom left) David McCarthy/Science Photo Library. 19: Image 100. 22: Photodisc.

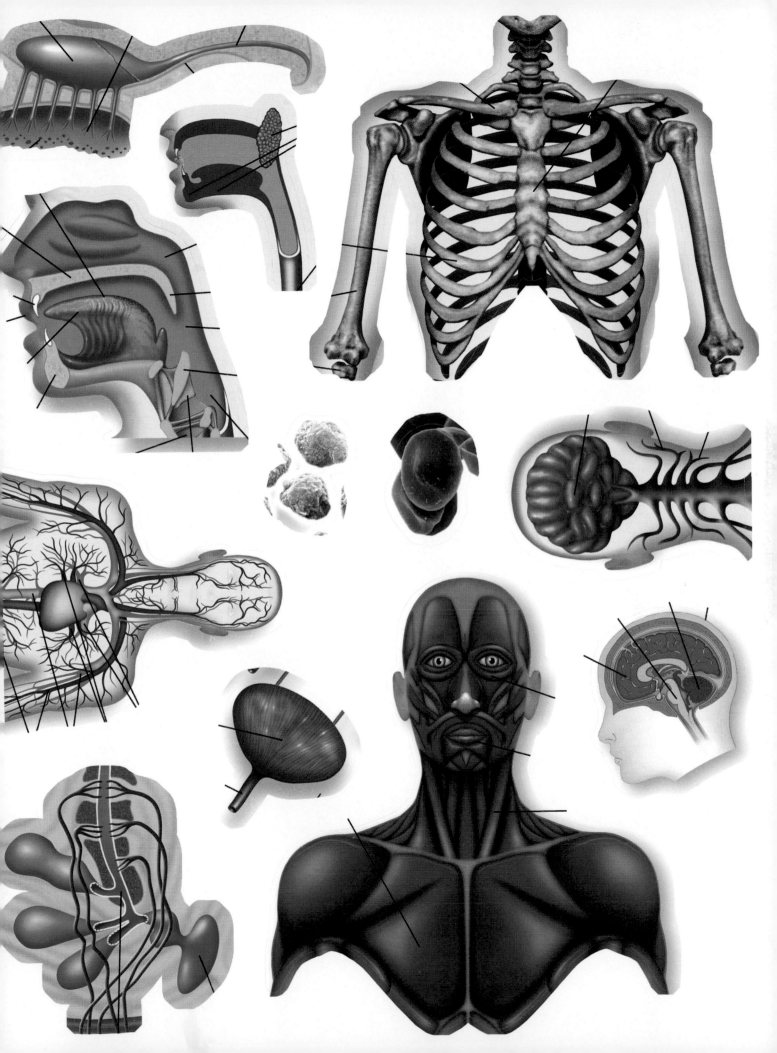

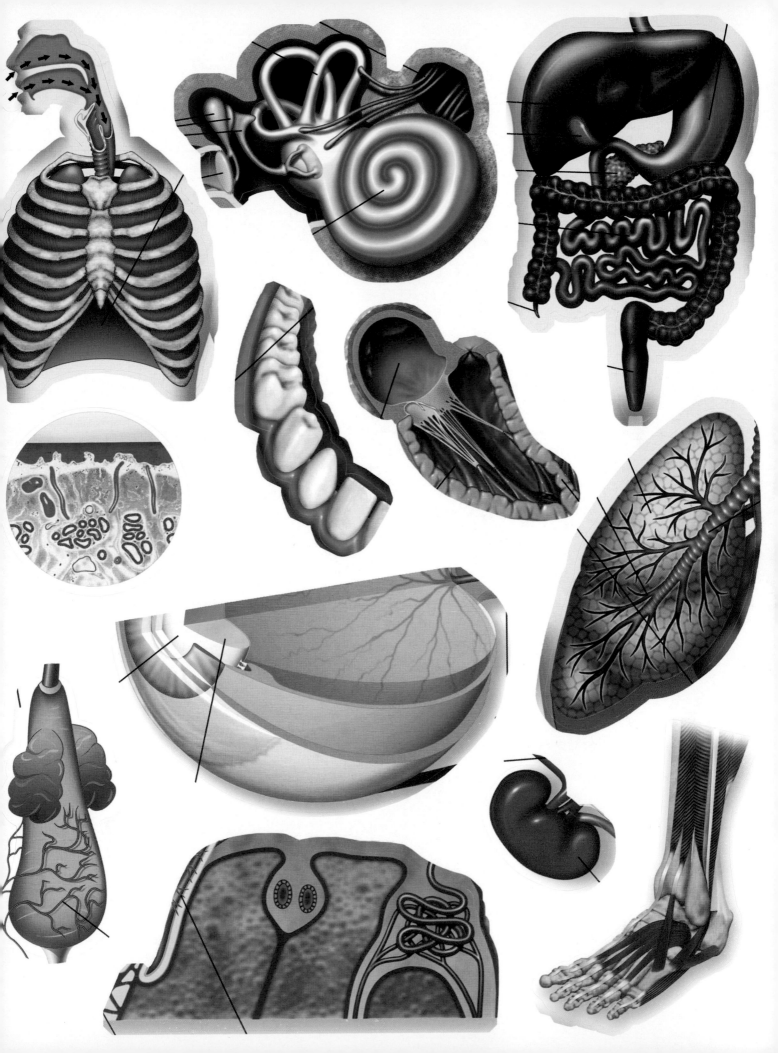